# Mulberry & Silk

SAGE
PRESS

Published in 2003

**SAGE PRESS,**
PO Box № 1, Rye, East Sussex TN36 6HN.
e.mail: sagepress.bm@btinternet.com www.sagepress.co.uk
© Sage Press 2003

Set in Palatine italic 9 on 11 point leading.
Display in Palatino Bold Italic 14 point.

*Design and Illustrations*
Chris Monk of Yellowduck Design & Illustration.

*Research and Text*
Stephanie Green and Zoë Meyer

*Publisher*
Mrs Bobby Meyer

Printed in England

0-9542297-3-8

Acknowledgements
The publisher wishes to warmly thank all those who helped in the making
of this little book. In particular, she wishes to mention the generosity of
Robert Gooden, who so kindly loaned her a valuable copy of Lady Zoë
Hart Dyke's book *So Spins the Silkworm* and Guy Hart Dyke of Lullingstone
Castle, Kent, who very kindly granted permission to quote from this book.
Also the librarian at Chelsea Library and the staff at Great Dixter.

# Mulberry & Silk

"Mulberry, **wisest** of trees",
Pliny, Roman historian.

Pliny was doubtless alluding to the fact that it is one of the
the slowest tree to put out new leaves in Spring, waiting
until all the frosts are over. Its generic name, morus, may
derive from the Latin for 'delay'.

'Of all the cultivated trees, the Mulberry is the last that
buds, which it never does until the cold weather is past, and
it is therefore called the wisest of trees. But when it begins to
put forth buds, it dispatches the business in
one night, and that with so much force, that
their breaking forth may be evidently
heard.' Pliny

The Mulberry was dedicated to
Minerva, the Roman Goddess of
Wisdom.

The name of the common Black
Mulberry, morus nigra, may be
derived from the Greek morus for
'black' and the Latin nigra – also
meaning 'black', both obviously
referring to the strikingly dense
colour of the ripened fruit
(which progresses from white,
through to reddish-black).

# Short and broad

**The Black Mulberry Tree** (or Bush as it is sometimes known) is short and broad in outline, never taller than 10m. Its dense, rather squat spreading head of branches is sometimes so wide that as the tree ages the branches have to be supported by props, making it look more ancient than it is. It can be a handsome tree and individual different specimens show a variety of strong outlines. Some writers, however, dismiss it sneeringly from the pantheon of noble and inspiring specimen trees for its lack of height, its twisting branches and short, often leaning, rough, gnarled trunk. Others though find it picturesque and love it for its rugged, unpredictable appearance.

Of the 20 or so existing species of Mulberry, there are three main ones, known after the distinguishing colour of their fruits – red, black and white.

Two species of Mulberry grow in Britain, the black and white, the black being the most widespread.

**The Black or Common Mulberry** (morus nigra) grows wild in northern Asia Minor, Armenia and the southern Caucasus region including Persia (now Iran). However, it has been cultivated for so many centuries in southern Europe, nobody can be sure of its native origin. Some say it was introduced from China along the old trading routes. Others believe it is a 'lost' native of southeastern Europe. It does best in the southern part of Britain, though its fruits can ripen as far north as South Sweden and up its west coast.

It was known in the Mediterranean Basin by both the Ancient Greeks and Romans, presumably having been introduced from Persia and has been cultivated in England since the sixteenth century, but there is always the possibility it was introduced here at a much earlier date by the Romans. Silkworms will thrive on its thick, heart-shaped leaves, with hairy undersides, but rearers only use it in cases of emergency or close to the end of the rearing season. The silk produced is coarse and a greater weight of leaf is required than with the White Mulberry.

**The White Mulberry**, (morus alba) is a much taller tree than the nigra and can reach 24m. It is a native of China and like many plants with similar origins can be grown successfully in southern England, but is quite rare to find. From a distance it has a narrower silhouette than the Black Mulberry, with an upright rather than a leaning trunk. However, the White Mulberry is of great historic and economic importance, as it is the leaves of this tree which provide the staple diet of the silk worm. It tends to be fairly disease-free and, most importantly, it leafs earlier, producing a greater total weight of leaves than the Black Mulberry and having a higher nutritive value, so requiring less per silkworm.

**The Red Mulberry** (morus rubra) is a native of the United States of America and very difficult to grow in Britain. It was introduced in the 18th century by the early colonialists in America in an unsuccessful attempt to create a silk industry.

**The French Mulberry** (callicarpa americana) is a shrub 1-2m high with blue flowers and violet fruit but is too tender for all but the mildest climates.

**The Weeping Mulberry** (morus alba pendula) is popular for its curtain-like branch structure in ornamental garden design. Its origins are in China but can thrive in southern Europe.

**The Paper Mulberry** (broussonetia papyrifera) is used in China and Japan to make paper.

# Paper

*The first paper, according to tradition, was made in 105AD from the bark of the Paper Mulberry tree, (or Rice-paper tree) in China. The invention of paper, of course, led to books and printing and the basis of our whole civilization. The dissemination of knowledge can safely be said to be linked to the wise Mulberry tree.*

*The bark fibres were scraped, soaked then beaten and treated with bleach. This mass was mixed with mucilage and spread in a thin layer to dry. Later it was smoothed with a hot iron. This process is still made by hand in parts of rural Japan and is used for lanterns, rough writing paper and umbrellas.*

*The modern Japanese sculptor, Isamu Noguchi, uses 'shoji' paper made by hand from boiled mulberry bark for his famous Akari lamps – inspired by the traditional lamps used by Japanese fishermen for night fishing - and of which there is a permanent exhibition at the Museum of Modern Art in New York.*

*There are two unrelated trees both called Rice-paper trees: one is the Paper Mulberry, (Broussonetia papyrifera) and belongs to the family Moraceae. The other belongs to the family Araliaceae (Tetrapanax papyriferus).*

# Silk

*'Patience and perseverance turn mulberry leaves into the silken robes of a queen'* Old Chinese proverb

*Without the Mulberry, which provides the leaves on which the silkworm thrives, there would be no silk.*

*Other alternatives have been tried in moments of desperation when the timing of the hatching of the silkworm eggs or 'graines' is earlier than the appearance of the new mulberry leaves. Chicory and lettuce leaves have been known to work for a short time, but are not always successful and never a replacement for the real thing.*

*Silk is one of the oldest known textile fibres and is made from the secretions of silk worms fed on White Mulberry (morus albus) leaves. Discovery of its manufacture was first made in China in around 2,500BC and remained a well-kept secret for many centuries.*

*Tradition has it that the potential of the cocoon and invention of the first silk reel was discovered by Hsi-ling-shi, the 14-year old bride of the Emperor Huang Ti. There are many different versions of the story handed down over the ages, but essentially the Emperor's wife is said to not only have reared silkworms in large numbers but also invented the first silk-weaving loom. His-ling-shi was so admired for her culture of silkworms that after her death altars were put up in her memory and she was known as the Goddess of the Silkworms.*

# China's secret

The secret of silk manufacture was jealously guarded by China. Diverting myths were even spread to deflect prying eyes. In one legend it was said that the silkworm first made its cocoon in the eyebrows of a beautiful maiden.

Nonetheless, the beautiful woven Chinese silks were exported and could be found at the Courts of Babylon and Ninevah, but anyone attempting to smuggle silkworm eggs or the seed of the Mulberry out of China would be risking inevitable death.

Finally the lure of this lustrous thread proved irresistible and by around 300 – 400 AD first Japan, and then India managed to 'crack the code'. There are many fanciful legends and stories relating how this happened and it is not difficult to imagine how tantalising it must have been to purchase these wonderful silk textiles and yet not know how to make them oneself. It is thought that most probably the knowledge was spread through war between Japan and Korea which inevitably brought with it large movements of peoples many of whom had been involved in the widespread art of sericulture in their home country.

# The Silk Road

Silk became not only the prerogative of Emperors and their Court, but also developed into a unique commodity which even lent its name to the trade route, the Silk Road, first used c. 100 BC. by the Han Dynasty to build up a lucrative trade with the western world. Caravans carried silk on camel back from deepest Central Asia to Syria where East and West met. Here the silk was bartered and exchanged for western luxuries.

Extraordinarily, the Ancient Persian courts used Chinese silks, unravelled and rewoven into Persian designs. When Darius III, King of Persia surrendered to Alexander the Great, Darius was dressed in such magnificent silk that it is said jealousy overcame Alexander and he demanded booty to the value of around £14 million ($7 million)- to be paid in silk.

Silk is mentioned also in the Old Testament, proving it was known in biblical times. Its creation is then thought to have spread to the Aegean Isles and it is known that the Island of Cos became a major trading post for large quantities of silk fabrics imported from China.

It became such a valuable commodity in Ancient Greece and Rome (traded with gold and silver) that Julius Caesar decided that he alone should be permitted to wear silk garments, thus denoting his high rank.  And as a concession his favourite officials were granted special permission to have the purple stripes on their togas woven in this  magic thread.

# Stolen secret

Silk manufacture remained virtually a monopoly shared by the Chinese and Persians until about 55 AD. This so infuriated the Roman Emperor Justinian I that he sent two Christian monks of Persian origin (of the Nestorian sect) posing as missionaries to Khotan in China where, at great risk to themselves, they stole some mulberry seeds and silkworm eggs and brought these back to Byzantium, secreted in their walking staffs – or so the story goes.

Certainly by the 6th century, the knowledge of silk manufacture or sericulture had at long last spread throughout Western Asia and into Europe.

Such was the desire for silk and its inherent economic promise that when in 947 AD the King of Sicily sacked Athens, Thebes and Corinth he calculatedly captured some silk-weavers to bring them back home to Palermo, where they taught his subjects the art of raising silkworms and weaving silk.

This was indeed a clever move – his subject were so adept that within twenty years Sicilian silk became prized both for its high quality and variety of beautiful weaving patterns.

# Silkworms

Silkworms are not worms at all but caterpillars! 'Silkworm' is in fact the common name for the larvae of several species of moths. The best known is the domesticated silkworm moth (Bombyx mori - Latin for mulberry-eating silkworm) which has been cultivated for centuries and is no longer known in the wild.

The silkworm manufactures fibre to produce a silk cocoon through a pair of silk glands, or sericteries, which are modified salivary glands.

The larvae, which hatch in about 10 days, are about 0.6 cm long, and feed on the leaves of White Mulberry, osage orange or lettuce. It is the caterpillars fed on mulberry leaves which produce the finest silk.

# Sericulture

Around six weeks after hatching the common silkworm stops eating the mulberry leaves and spins its cocoon. If allowed to complete its pupation period, (about two weeks) it emerges as an adult moth. However, emergence tears the silken cocoon beyond commercial use, so most of the silkworms are killed by heat, either by immersion in boiling water or by drying in ovens. Only enough adult moths are allowed to emerge, to ensure continuation of the species.

# Other Uses

## Aquaculture - Fish farming in China

*Although the secrets of fine silk-making were now known to the West, the industrious Chinese continued their own thriving and sophisticated sericulture, perfected over a period of 2,000 years and more and providing a sustainable source of rural employment for women. In the late 19th century about half the population of South China were thought to have been working in the booming silk industry and it was not wiped out until the depression of the 1930's.*

*There were vast plantations of mulberry trees producing leaves to feed the silkworms and forming an integral part of a cleverly devised, perfect ecological cycle, linking it with fish farming and duck rearing to produce brilliant results all round.*

*Both the silkworm waste and the duck droppings provided food for the fish in their rearing ponds. Then once a year the fish were sold and the ponds drained. The fish waste and silt were collected and used to fertilize the mulberry trees, thus producing high quality trees, silkworms, ducks and fish.*

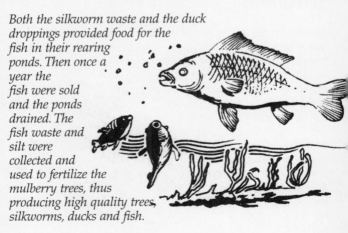

# Royal patronage

*'There is scarcely an old garden or gentleman's seat throughout the country, which can be traced back to the seventeenth century, in which a Mulberry tree is not to be found.'* Loudon

There had been many attempts to establish a silk industry in England - starting in the 14th century and always encouraged by the reigning monarch. However, it was James I of England (James VI of Scotland), understanding the economical potential which sericulture could release, who made the first large-scale, organised effort to enrich the nation by introducing sericulture on a systematic basis. James wanted to break the French monopoly in silk. There had been a flood of Hugenot refugees into the country, many settling in London where they soon established a thriving silk-weaving industry in Spitalfields.

But it was expensive to import the raw silk yarn, so thousands of Mulberry trees were brought from France and free seeds were distributed. Silkworm eggs were imported from Italy and experimental rearings carried out. In 1608 an edict was passed urging the Lord Lieutenants of the shires of England: *'To persuade and require such as are of ability to buy and distribute in that County the number of ten thousand Mulberry plants which shall be delivered to them at our City of -, at the rate of 3 farthings the plant, or at 6s the hundred containing five score plants.'*

The Mulberries and silkworms flourished and the King even planted a Mulberry plantation near his palace on what is thought may have been the present site of Buckingham Palace. But things appear to have gone wrong. It seems he chose to plant the Black Mulberry which is slow growing and less suitable. Soon the diarist, John Evelyn, wrote of the mulberry gardens as being merely pleasure gardens for the public to visit and enjoy.

## Silk in the American Colonies

**Silkworm rearing room**

The efforts made by the far-sighted King James to establish silk in Virginia and Georgia had greater success, albeit using somewhat arm-twisting tactics: every colonist setting out for Virginia was given a book on sericulture by Jean Bondeil and anyone not planting 10 Mulberry trees per 100 acres of land owned could be fined. Above all James wanted to steer the colonists towards silk as a way of stopping them growing tobacco, which he abhorred.

Later, in the early 18th century, free land was offered to
settlers as an incentive, provided they planted 100 Mulberry
trees per 10 acres. Mulberry seed and silkworm eggs were
provided free and even an Italian expert was on hand to train
them. Records show that in 1759 the Colony exported over
10,000 pounds in weight of raw silk. Sadly cotton turned out
to be more lucrative a crop and interest in sericulture waned.

## Shakespeare's Mulberry

A famous Mulberry in Shakespeare's garden in New Place,
Stratford-upon-Avon, was said to have been taken by
Shakespeare from James I's garden in 1609 and there are
descendants from this tree at Kew Gardens today. The tree
was celebrated in a poem by Dibdin.

However, Shakespeare's tree was cut down in 1752 by the Rev.
Mr. Gastrell, the then
owner of New Place, in
exasperation at the
numbers of admirers
of the Bard who
came to see the
tree and 'to
save himself
the trouble
of showing
(them)
the
tree'.

Many snuff boxes were made out of the remains of the tree and other mementoes, some inscribed with the words, *Memento Mori* ('Remember Death'): a pun on the latin for the Mulberry, *morus*.

## Garrick's Cup

Ten years later, when the Freedom of the City was bestowed on the famous actor-manager Garrick, it is said that the document was presented inside a casket made from the wood of Shakespeare's Mulberry. At the Shakespeare Jubilee, Garrick held a cup also made from the same wood and recited verses, composed by himself, in Shakespeare's honour. Garrick grew a Mulberry tree from a slip of it in his own garden and scion from this now grows in Shakespeare's garden.

# The Romans

*References in Virgil's* Georgics *(II.v.121), show that Mulberry trees abounded in Italy at this time. They ate the juicy mulberries at feasts and Horace in his* Satires *(Sat. ii.) recommended that the fruit be gathered before sunset. Virgil's name for the tree,* sanguinea morus, *(the 'bloody' morus) refers to the red colour of the fruit and the legend of Pyramus and Thisbe (q.v.)*

*By Virgil's death in 19 BC, the role of the silkworm in the production of silk was still unknown to the Romans, who thought that it was solely due to the Mulberry leaves.*

*Excavations in Pompeii have revealed a Black Mulberry in the peristyle of 'The House of the Bull' and mulberry leaves are also represented in a mosaic in 'The House of the Faun'.*

# Pyramus and Thisbe

*The Roman poet, Ovid, recounted in* Metamorphoses *the ancient Babylonian story of the two young lovers, Pyramus and Thisbe, who fell in love but were forbidden to marry. They would converse through a crack in the wall.*

They decide to meet by the tomb of Ninus under a White Mulberry tree.

Arriving first, Thisbe sees a lion with bloody jaws from a recent kill and flees, dropping her veil which the lion mauls. Pyramus appears and, seeing the bloody veil, wrongly concludes Thisbe is dead. He draws his sword and kills himself, blood spurting on the Mulberry and staining the white fruit purple. Thisbe then discovers Pyramus' body and kills herself. The Romans used this story to explain the changing colour of Mulberry fruit.

## Medicinal Uses

'Boil the green leaves from the mulberry tree and drink the infusion.'Taylor MSS, East Harling, Norfolk)

In East Anglia the leaves of the Mulberry were used as a cure for diarrhoea.

In modern medicine the Mulberry is still used to flavour or colour other medicines, syrups in particular,  and is an official drug of the British Pharmacopoeia. It colours dark violet or purple with a faint odour and acid-saccharine taste.

Used as a gargle it can soothe sore throats though it is chiefly used as an adjuvant rather than for its expectorant and slightly laxative effects as recommended by Gerard:

'The barke of the root is bitter, hot and drie, and hath a scouring faculty: the decoction hereof doth open the stoppings of the liver and spleen; it purgeth the belly, and driveth forth wormes'.

In the East, the bark of morus nigra is anthelmintic
and is used to expel tape worm. The root-bark of
morus indica (Rumph) is used under the name
of San-pai-p'i as a diuretic and expectorant.

The Morinda tinctoria, or Indian Mulberry
is used by African aborigines for medicine
but there is no reliable evidence of its
efficacy. In the islands of Meshima, Japan, a
parasitic fungus, Meshimakobu, growing on
the old stems of Mulberry trees, is used for
medicine.

In Kabul it is dried on the tops of houses then
pounded to a fine powder and mixed with flour for
bread.

## Proverbs

'In the Western Counties it is asserted that frost ceases as
soon as the mulberry tree bursts into leaf.'
T.F. Thiselton Dyer, The Folklore of Plants.

'With Time, and Art, the Mulberry Leafs grow to be sattin'.
Howell, 1659

'What will not time and toil? - by these a worm.
Will into silk a mulberry leaf transform'.
ABP. Trench, Poems; Proverbs, Turkish and Persian,
xxi.303.

## Folklore

In East Anglia blackberries were known as Mulberries: 'Only people of substance had their mulberry trees. The ordinary people had to be content with the bramble' the poor man's fruit'. G.E. Evans, Aspects of Oral Tradition, 1969.

'Here we go round the Mulberry Bush,
The Mulberry Bush, the Mulberry Bush,
Here we go round the Mulberry Bush,
On a cold and frosty morning'.
A old children's nursery rhyme still popular today.

## Mulberry Fruit

The mature fruits are loganberry-like in shape and size. Commercially, mulberries have a limited use as they are difficult to handle. In Turkey the farmers shake the trees to allow the ripened fruit to fall onto cloths spread below and then leave them to dry in the sun. These then provide an excellent source of Vitamin C during the winter months.

Mulberry wine is said to resemble port in taste. In Devon mulberries were sometimes mixed with cider during fermentation. In Greece, also, mulberries were fermented, to make an alcoholic drink. Morat, made from mulberries and honey was a favourite drink of the Anglo-Saxons, according

to Sir Walter Scott in Ivanhoe. However, there is some doubt
that the morum of the Anglo-Saxon Vocabularies was indeed
mulberry. There is a school of thought which claims they were
in fact blackberries.

'Mulberries are not much desired to be eaten, although they
be somewhat pleasant both for that they stain their fingers
and lips that eat them, and do quickly putrefie in the
stomach, if they be not taken before meat.' Parkinson

Victorians made the fruit into mulberry wine, tarts, jams and
jellies. The fruit is sour until black and ripe when it has a
pleasant sub-acid or sweet-sour taste. The White Mulberry
fruit never becomes as good to eat as the Black Mulberry.
Opinion is divided as to their taste. Parkinson evidently
disliked them.

## Victorian Confusion

Red, blue, black, yellow and white The Victorians were
confused by the different colours of the mulberry fruits.
A letter to The Gardeners' Chronicle in 1844 asked:

'Col. Davidson, in his Travels in India lately published,
mentions 4 or 5 different sorts of mulberries – red, blue, black,
yellow and white. What are these? Only one edible kind is
known in this country'.

The confusion arose not only because of the two species of
Mulberry introduced into Britain, the Black and the White
Mulberry trees but because the fruits of both trees change colour
as they ripen. The fruit of the Black Mulberry is first green,
then white and finally turns orange or scarlet by mid-summer.
It continues to darken , eventually becoming a blackish-red.

To add to the puzzlement mature and immature fruits can be found on the same tree at the same time, depending on the direction of the sun.

The fruit of the White Mulberry is much paler and for most of the summer remains almost white, hence the tree's name. In the autumn it turns yellow, pink or purple when ripe but never reaches the dark colour of the Black Mulberry.

## Sex-Change

The flowers of the Black Mulberry tree appear in late spring as insignificant yellow-green catkins. The male catkins are about 2.5 cm and the females half that size.

The Victorians noticed that the catkins of the same tree could change sex according to climate.

Mr Knight, a correspondent in The Gardeners' Chronicle in 1844, noted: 'The effect of an excessively high temperature, is to cause in unisexual plants, the production of male flowers only, while a very low temperature produces the opposite result.'

# Recipes

### Black Mulberry Wine

*Ripe Mulberries*
*Boiling water*
*3 lb sugar to each gallon*
*1 clove per bottle*
*Small sugar lump per bottle*

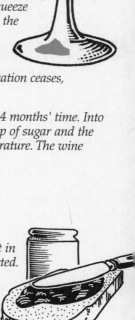

*For each gallon of ripe mulberries, pour 1 gallon of*
*boiling water and let stand for 2 days. Squeeze*
*all through a hair sieve or bag. Wash out the*
*tub or jar and return the liquor to it, and*
*add sugar; stir until quite dissolved then*
*put liquor into a jar or cask. Let the cask*
*be raised a little on one side until fermentation ceases,*
*then bung down.*

*If the liquor be clean it may be bottled in 4 months' time. Into*
*each bottle put one clove and a small lump of sugar and the*
*bottles should be kept at a medium temperature. The wine*
*may be used in a year from bottling.*

### Mulberry Jam

*4lb of mulberries*
*3lb of sugar*

*Put 1lb of mulberries in a jar and stand it in*
*a pan of hot water until the juice is extracted.*
*Strain them and put the juice into a*
*preserving pan with 3 lb of sugar. Boil it*
*and remove scum. Put in 3 lb of*
*mulberries and let them stand in the*

syrup until thoroughly warm then set the pan back on the ring and boil them gently for a short time, stirring all the time and taking care not to break the fruit. Take the pan off the ring and let it stand in the syrup all night. The next morning put back on the ring and boil gently till stiff. The jam can taste rather acid unless very ripe fruit are used.

## Famous Mulberry trees in Britain

'... a mulberry tree groweth in divers gardens in England' Dr. William Turner 'the Father of English Botany' who is known to have planted two Mulberries at Syon House, Middlesex.

The earliest known planting of a Mulberry was at Syon House in 1548. There are many ancient specimens scattered all over the country, to which pubs and inns named 'The Mulberry Tree' still bear testimony today. Mulberries can frequently be seen at houses open to the public, Charlton House and Hogarth House being but two of many.

### Great Dixter, East Sussex

A pair of Mulberries were planted around 1912 in the newly-created garden designed by Sir Edwin Lutyens for the parents of the present owner, Christopher Lloyd. Sadly, one was felled by the great storm in 1987 and although the other was damaged, it survived as a tribute to the tree's ability to re-generate.

Skilled pruning has resulted in an exceptionally well-shaped crown, quite unlike the usual gnarled and bowed specimens seen in English gardens. According to the Head Gardener, Fergus Garrett, it is quite easy to propagate this tree vegetally, using lengths of branches known as 'truncheons'. At Great Dixter the mulberry fruit is used constantly, mulberry steamed pudding being an all-time favourite of the family.

Many Mulberries are not as long-lived as commonly thought, although they can quickly look very ancient because of their leaning habit and need to be propped up. However, in London there are some truly old survivors of 17th-18th century attempts to create mulberry orchards to support the silk industry. Vestiges of these plantings are echoed in London's Chelsea area in street names such as Mulberry Walk. It is said there are still fruit-bearing ancient mulberries dating back to that time around the Chelsea Park Gardens area, lying as they do on what was the southern boundary of Chelsea Park, once part of Sir Thomas More's 40 acre estate.

'A proper tree for noble English gardens…' the Mulberry tree as described by a 12th century monk from Cirencester.

The site of the grand house and gardens belonging to Sir Thomas More overlooking the river at Chelsea, part of which is now occupied by the The Mulberry Tree Convent still has an ancient Mulberry tree under which Sir Thomas and family ' frequently enjoyed witty and tender conversations beneath its shelter…'

The 18th century nurseryman and pioneer hybridiser, Thomas Fairchild noted thriving Mulberry trees on his walks through London. Writing in The City Gardener he described a pair outside the Clothworkers Hall as having 'stood there many years, and bear plentifully and ripen very well'. In present-day Ludgate Hill, close to the Fleet Ditch he comments on two large Mulberry tress in a yard only some 16 ft square, outside Sam's Coffee House.

# Silken Thread Around the Globe

Silk production and the planting of Mulberry orchards has over the centuries captured the imagination of leaders, monarchs and entrepreneurs around the world. It is frequently seen as a fairly low-cost job and wealth creation scheme but despite determination and grand-scale organisation, as with the French and their ambitious mulberry planting schemes, it is often affected by wars, the introduction of new products or disease. For China it did indeed become a huge industry until well into the 20th century and the French and Italians are to this day renowned for their fine silks. Today, China, Japan and India are the leading silk producers.

But the rearing of silkworms requires great skill and patience and history shows there are many unexpected hurdles to overcome. The Mulberries are very adaptable and not difficult to grow, although the timing of the hatching silkworms and the first leaves on the Mulberry trees can be fraught. And there have also been diseases which have wiped out all the silkworm brood, as happened in the mid-19th century when a mysterious disease known as 'pebrine' wiped out all the silk worms in France and spread like wildfire around the rest of Europe and the Middle East. The industry was finally saved from total extinction in the 1860s by the work of a young scientist employed by the French government, who discovered the disease was hereditary and could by identified at the egg stage.

And walking round Chelsea today, to recall those times there are still streets with names such as Mulberry Walk and old houses with Mulberries in their gardens.

Many English pubs throughout the country are named 'The Mulberry Tree'.

There are so many stories through the centuries describing similar efforts to set up a local silk-production industry, using sophisticated incentives and training schemes. More recently, a particularly fascinating instance was in Germany. In 1936, with war looming on the horizon, the German government set up a Four Year Sericultural Plan to prevent any raw silk shortages. 100 million Mulberries were planted and 10 new spinning mills set up. Through this project evolved a new textile product known as viscose and made from Mulberry wood pulp.

Apart from discovering bi-products whilst producing the silk itself, there have been efforts to rear silkworms on local trees where Mulberries are difficult to grow, as in the Soviet Union where they claimed to have produced a variety of silkworm which lives off birch leaves. And in Japan producers have succeeded in forcing silkworms to spin a flat surface, eliminating the cocoons and the costly process of stifling the cocoons to kill the chrysalides.

## Lullingstone Silk Farm

Whilst the German Government was occupied setting up their silk industry an extraordinary English lady was taking the first steps to set up a silk farm of her own in her husband's ancestral home, Lullingstone Castle, in Kent. Her fascination for rearing silkworms had started much earlier when as a small girl she had been rearing them in drawers and boxes.

The story of Zoë Lady Hart Dyke and her adventures in silk production can be read in her book *So Spins the Silkworm* — Rockliff, 1949, which today is out of print, but worth hunting down. Despite many setbacks, the farm grew and thrived and it was to produce silk for the coronation dresses of Queen Elizabeth and Queen Elizabeth II, as well as for the train and the wedding dress of Queen Elizabeth II at her wedding to Prince Philip. It became a tradition to supply silk for royal occasions including christening gowns for four royal babies and the robes for the Investiture of the Prince of Wales.

Lullingstone Silk Farm attracted many thousands of visitors each year and was sold in 1977 to Robert and Rosemary Goodden. Its was moved to their home at Compton House in Dorset and now forms part of Worldwide Butterflies which is a major attraction. Visitors to the silk farm can see the rearing and reeling of pure English silk. Adults and children alike are fascinated to watch the process from egg to the finished hank of silk yarn.

# The Collectors' Series of Trees

## Are you collecting… ?

"… and a very charming book it is…"
Roy Lancaster, on MONKEY PUZZLE

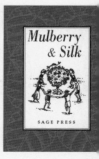

**T**REES STIR passions in us all, whether from climbing them in our youth or just from their natural beauty, we all feel a deep affinity with these majestic, timeless, immobile forms.

How better to deepen our love for trees than a series of books celebrating this unique heritage, the amusing and well-balanced text complimented by Chris Monk's delightfully quirky illustrations.

# Botanical Notes

**Common name**: *Mulberry Tree or Bush*

**Botanical Name**:
*morus*

**Family**:
*Moraceae*

**Relatives**:
*Other latex-bearing woody plants such as ficus (fig), hemp(marijuana) and breadfruit. Another important member of the family is osage orange.*

**Branches**:
*The branches are wider than its height, twisting with a rugged appearance. Often they have to be supported in old age.*

**Size**:
*The Black Mulberry (morus nigra) reaches 9m – 10m. The White Mulberry (morus alba) is taller, sometimes up to 15m high .*

**Growth**:
*Morus nigra (Black Mulberry) is slow growing. Morus alba (White Mulberry) is faster. The trunk of the black variety is short and often leans, whereas the white variety has a taller, straighter trunk.*

**Wood**:
*The wood is very springy and used by the Japanese to make sporting equipment and, more special, for making the 'chashanku', the green tea scoop used in the semi-formal tea ceremony (if formal it would be made of ivory). Mulberry twigs are made into baskets.*

## Leaves:

The leaves of the black Mulberry can vary enormously.

*Black Mulberry leaf*

They are usually heart-shaped with serrated margins and pointed tips but on young shoots or copicced trees, they can be deeply-lobed like fig leaves. Indeed the leaves can be so different that some nurserymen have been erroneously accused of supplying the wrong tree! Identification can be assured by the rough hairy texture, even coarse downiness of the leaf. The leaves of the White Mulberry are similar to the Black, but have a greater tendency to be lobed and are rounded rather than heart-shaped. They are thinner, softer and hairless.

*White Mulberry leaf*

## Fruit:

The fruits are multiple, a cluster structure known as syncarps. Each fruit contains a single nutlet but as they do not open they are known as drupes (as are plums and cherries). Much loved by birds.

## Bark:

The bark of the Black Mulberry is orange-brown with deep stringy fissures, becoming gnarled in old age. On old White Mulberries the bark is similar, although in younger trees it is pinkish-brown or grey.

## Flowers:

Male and female catkins can be found on the same tree and so it is self-fertile. The male catkins are about 2.5 cm and the females are half that. They appear in late spring as yellow-green catkins on hairy stalks in the leaf axis.

The mulberry is a dicot, sprouting embryo seed leaves that do not become foliage leaves but provide food for the new seedling.

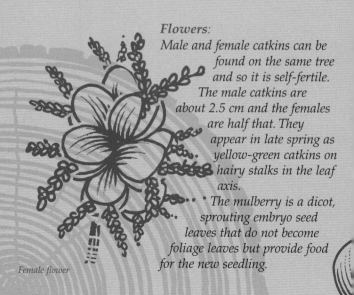

*Female flower*

Layers made in the autumn
will root in twelve months.
Cuttings of young wood,
up to 3m long  and known
as 'truncheons', planted
late in the year, will root
more quickly if put under
glass. Evaporation can be
prevented by wrapping the
stem above ground with
moss — all but the upper
pair of buds.

The Mulberry can also be
grown from seed, which
should be sown in gentle
heat or in the open, early
in the year and will
produce seedlings by the
autumn.

Mulberry trees do not bear
fruit for at least 15 years.

### Cultivation:

Mulberry trees like
warm, well-drained loamy
soil. No pruning is
required except for the
removal of dead or
crossing branches. The tree
will benefit from occasional
applications of manure.

In Japan it has proved very
adaptable to a wide variety
of local conditions and
there about 700 types
growing from tropical
to very dry zones, at sea
level to up to 3,300m.

*Detail of female flower*

## In the same series

*Ash*
*Box*
*Caring for Box*
*Cedar of Lebanon*
*Fig*
*Hawthorn*
*Holly*
*Monkey Puzzle*
*Oak*
*Sitka Spruce*
*Yew*

## Future Titles

**Black Poplar**
**Wild Service Tree**
**Willow for Basketmakers**

## Also available

The Puzzle Puzzle Jigsaw

If you enjoyed this title and would like to buy any
of the above titles or require further information
please contact

### SAGE PRESS

PO Box № 1, Rye, East Sussex TN36 6HN.
e-mail: sagepress.bm@btinternet.com
www.sagepress.co.uk